C000052554

This book belongs to:

Sophie Baggaley

Birthday: September   Age: 7

My favourite
Rainbow Magic fairy is:

Chloe the Topaz Fairy

Stick a smiley photo of yourself in
this flower or draw a self-portrait:

ORCHARD BOOKS
338 Euston Road, London NW1 3BH
Orchard Books Australia
Level 17/207 Kent Street, Sydney, NSW 2000

First published in 2010 by Orchard Books.

© 2010 Rainbow Magic Limited.
A HIT Entertainment company. Rainbow Magic
is a trademark of Rainbow Magic Limited.
Reg. U.S. Pat. & Tm. Off. And other countries.

Fairy illustrations on cover © Orchard Books.
All interior fairy illustrations © Georgie Ripper, with the exception of
Samantha the Swimming Fairy and Rihanna the Seahorse Fairy on
page 11, all illustrations on pages 12-15, 18, 20-21, 26-27, 30-31, 38,
42-45, 48-49, 50-51, 53, Sophia the Snow Swan Fairy on page 22,
Alice the Tennis Fairy and Caitlin the Ice Bear Fairy on page 24,
Francesca the Football Fairy, Samantha the Swimming Fairy and
Sadie the Saxophone Fairy on pages 36-37, Mia the Bridesmaid Fairy
on page 52 and Fiona the Flute Fairy on page 55. These and all other
illustrations © Orchard Books, based on underlying copyright owned
by Georgie Ripper.

A CIP catalogue record for this book is available
from the British Library.

ISBN 978 1 40830 811 0

1 3 5 7 9 10 8 6 4 2

Printed in Italy
Orchard Books is a division of Hachette Children's Books,
an Hachette UK company.

www.hachette.co.uk

RAINBOW magic®

Holiday Activity Annual

Contents

7   Rainbow Magic Summer Sunshine Code

8   Summertime Fun!

10   June Birthday Girls

11   Sweet as Honey

12   A Magical Secret

16   July Birthday Girls

17   Best Friends Forever!

18   Spot the Difference

19   Goblin Tangle

20   Eye Spy

22   Spot the Fairies!

23   A Wand that goes Whoosh!

24   The Luckiest Fairy

25   Special Spells

26   Magical Animals and their Fairies!

28   Petal Puzzle

29   Pink Petals!

30   Fairy Ring Pairs

32   Fairyland Treasure Hunt

34   August Birthday Girls

35   Goldie's Summer Refresher!

36   Race from the Rain!

38   Melodie's Musical Maze

39   Dress Design

40   September Birthday Girls

41   Almost Bedtime!

42   Magical Ribbon Rescue

46   Animal Search

47   Lemon Scented Secrets

48   A Shivery Scene

51   A Freezing Flag

52   Beautiful Bridesmaid

53   Summer Memories

54   Magical Masks

55   More Fairy Magic!

56   Garden Fun

57   Did You Know...

58   Rainbow Magic!

60   How to be a Good Fairy

61   Answers

Rainbow Magic
Summer Sunshine Code

The Rainbow Magic fairies have a special code for the holidays. It helps them all have a happy summer! The Sunshine Code is easy to remember, because it spells out the word RAINBOW.

R is for rain. We adore visits from Goldie the Sunshine Fairy but we don't mind the occasional day with Hayley the Rain Fairy!

A is for adventure. The summer months are a great time to get out and about and discover new things with your friends.

I is for include. Always include all your friends if you are planning something fun like a picnic or a bike ride. No one likes to be left out! Polly the Party Fun Fairy is good at remembering everyone at her parties!

N is for never forget. On hot sunny days never forget your hat and your sun cream. Summer the Holiday Fairy will help you remember!

B is for be thoughtful. Always think of your friends and what they like to do.

O is for on your own. Don't be afraid to spend time alone every now and then. It's a great opportunity to read or get creative with crafts. Just ask Grace the Glitter Fairy!

W is for willing to help. Always offer to help your friends and family during the holidays. Pippa the Poppy Fairy offers to help the other Petal Fairies during the long summer months.

Summertime Fun!

The Rainbow Magic fairies love the warm summer months, but they all have different reasons why.

Sky
the Blue Fairy

I love making the sky as blue as me.

Goldie
the Sunshine Fairy

Goldie the Sunshine Fairy

I love bringing warm sunshine to all my fairy friends!

Abigail
the Breeze Fairy

Sometimes a cooling breeze is just the thing on a hot afternoon.

Phoebe
the Fashion Fairy

It's nice to wear summery clothes in ice-cream colours!

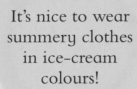

Lucy
the Diamond Fairy

I can really glitter and gleam on sunny days!

Penny
the Pony Fairy

There's nothing like riding Glitter along a sunny beach.

Ella
the Rose Fairy

My blooms are at their scented best on a summer's day.

Sienna
the Saturday Fairy

Sunny Saturdays are glorious!

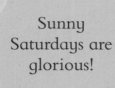

Danielle
the Daisy Fairy

This is the perfect time to learn how to make a daisy chain!

Samantha
the Swimming Fairy

Saskia
the Salsa Fairy

My dance is best performed on a warm summer's evening!

I love inviting the other Sporty Fairies to join me for a dip!

Rihanna
the Seahorse Fairy

Peer carefully into sunny rockpools and maybe you'll spot one of my friends!

Summer
the Holiday Fairy

I am the luckiest fairy of all. Who doesn't look forward to the summer holidays?

Jack Frost

I don't look forward to the summer. I might melt!

9

June Birthday Girls

Do you know anyone with a birthday in June? Sunny June days are perfect for sharing ripe strawberries and giggles!

1st-12th
Ruby the Red Fairy

These birthday girls should get close to nature this year. Secrets swapped with friends in a fairy ring at the bottom of a summer's garden will give you some unforgettable memories!

13th-22nd
India the Moonstone Fairy

You're a dreamer – your head is often in the clouds! Use your amazing imagination and write stories, poems and plays in the months ahead.

23rd-30th
Phoebe the Fashion Fairy

Your cute fashion sense always turns heads. Why not try customising your own clothes this year? Your fab style could work wonders with an old necklace or forgotten T-shirt!

Birthstone

India's enchanting moonstone glows all the colours of the rainbow. Girls born in June are very lucky to have such a magical birthstone!

Sweet as Honey

Saffron the Yellow Fairy is very fond of her buzzy friend, Queenie. Find your sunniest colours for this pretty picture.

A Magical Secret

Rachel and Kirsty were loving their time at adventure camp. Not only were they sleeping in a tent, canoeing with their friends and having great fun, but they were also on the lookout for Magical Animals!

At the start of their holiday, the King and Queen of Fairyland had asked for their help. These seven young Magical Animals had amazing powers which helped to spread the kind of magic that humans as well as fairies could possess – the wonderful gifts of imagination, good luck, humour, friendship, compassion, healing and courage.

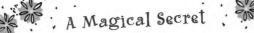

The seven Magical Animal Fairies spent a whole year training these youngsters before they returned them to their families in Fairyland, ready to use their special talents to help everyone in both the human and the fairy worlds. However, spiteful Jack Frost was determined to put a stop to all this, because he wanted everyone to be as lonely and miserable as him. So he and his naughty goblin servants had kidnapped the Magical Animals and taken them to his Ice Castle.

Luckily, the little animals had managed to escape, and now they had hidden themselves away in the human world. Rachel and Kirsty were determined to find all seven Magical Animals before Jack Frost and his goblins did, and return them to Fairyland.

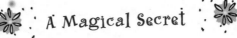

"We've done quite well so far, haven't we, Kirsty?" Rachel remarked. "We've found Ashley's dragon, Lara's black cat and Erin's firebird."

"I just hope we find the others before the end of the week," whispered Kirsty.

One morning, the girls set off for Adventure Lake to go canoeing.

"I'm going to try to keep my feet dry this time!" laughed Kirsty, as they clambered into their seats and pushed themselves away from the bank.

As they began to row across the water they spotted another canoe just ahead of them. Kirsty frowned as she stared at the little boat. The three passengers looked very familiar!

"Rachel!" Kirsty whispered urgently. "Goblins!"

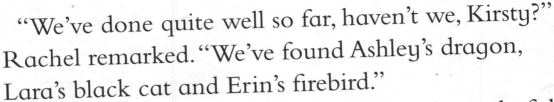

The goblins were holding a large fishing net, ready to fling it into the water.

"Now!" shouted the biggest goblin. They tried to toss the net into the water, but they all got tangled up. The goblins shrieked with fury as the boat rocked violently from side to side. Eventually they gathered up the net again and threw it into the water. After a moment they began pulling it in.

"We've caught something!" the biggest goblin shrieked triumphantly. It was a wriggling silver fish. "Is this a seahorse?" he asked the others.

"The goblins are looking for Rihanna's Magic Seahorse!" Kirsty whispered excitedly. Suddenly, the lake around them was filled with sparkling, rainbow-coloured bubbles. A second later a tiny fairy burst from the water with a shimmering splash and hovered in the air above them. "Hello," the fairy called. "I'm Rihanna the Seahorse Fairy!"

You can read more about this adventure in *Rihanna the Seahorse Fairy*

July Birthday Girls

Anyone with a birthday in July is very lucky. This is just the *right* month for ice creams!

1st-12th
Goldie the Sunshine Fairy

You're as bright as a sunbeam – no one can resist all the kind and thoughtful things you do. This year it's your turn to be treated, as your friends show you just how much you mean to them, too!

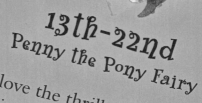

13th-22nd
Penny the Pony Fairy

You love the thrill of adventure – life is a rollercoaster whenever you're in charge! Slow down this year; it's nice to take things easy some of the time!

23rd-31st
Lauren the Puppy Fairy

If you're not allowed to have the pet you've always wished for, don't despair! Volunteer to care for the school hamster or help friends look after their animals – you're destined to make a pet pal.

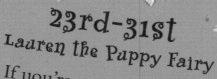

Birthstone

The majestic ruby is the birthstone for all those born in July. The ruby is often associated with power and confidence!

Best Friends Forever!

Do you have a friend with a birthday coming up? Or perhaps you'd like to make a thank-you card, or just a card to say hello. Try making this gorgeous card for someone special.

You will need:

Thin white card
Pencil
Scissors
Felt-tip pens or crayons

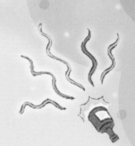

1 Take a sheet of card and fold it neatly in half. Press down along the fold and then open out the sheet again.

2 Flatten the card in front of you, then use a pencil to draw a heart. Make sure that the top half of the heart sits above the fold line and the other half below.

3 Ask a grown-up to help you cut carefully around the top half of the heart. Only cut out the parts of the heart that appear above the fold line.

4 Fold the card flat, then use your favourite felt-tips or crayons to colour the heart in.

5 When you've finished colouring, fold the card back along the crease. Your beautiful heart will pop up at the top!

Try using glittery gel pens or adding stickers to create extra sparkle!

Spot the Difference

Doesn't this picture make you hungry? Here are two peckish Sporty Fairies stopping for a yummy picnic. Can you spot five differences between the pictures? Circle them on the bottom picture.

Goblin Tangle

Jack Frost is not happy. His silly goblins have managed to get themselves into a terrible tangle! Can you count how many goblins there are?

Eye Spy

Feast your eyes on this wonderful scene of the Fairyland Palace Gardens. Everyone is having a fantastic time, tending the gardens and enjoying the sunshine. Look at the picture carefully and tick the boxes when you have found everything listed.

Can you spot:

One mole ✓

Three butterflies ✓

Seven magic wands ✓

Two birds ✓

Eight carrots ✓

One dolphin ✓

Five bumblebees ✓

and if you look really carefully . . .
Two goblins!

Spot the Fairies!

The fabulous fairies at the top of the page appear in exactly the same order on only one of the below rows. Can you find them and circle them?

Row C

Row A

Row B

Row C

Row D

22

A Wand that goes Whoosh!

Every Rainbow Magic fairy has an enchanted wand! Here's how to make your own signature wand – all you need are nimble fingers and a mind for magic.

You will need:
Newspapers
A wooden chopstick
Poster paint
Paintbrush
Thin satin ribbon
Scissors
Spray adhesive
Glitter

1. Lay out some old newspapers and then paint the chopstick.

2. When the chopstick has dried, pick out a length of satin ribbon in a pretty colour.

3. Spiral the ribbon up and down the wand. Start from the wide end of the chopstick and leave 20 cm of ribbon spare (a). When you wind the ribbon back to the base, leave another 20 cm extra before tying the ends in a bow (b).

4. Ask a grown-up to lightly cover the entire wand in spray adhesive.

5. Sprinkle glitter up and down the length of the wand and shake off the excess. Your sparkly wand is ready to dazzle your friends!

Why not try decorating your wand? silk flowers, strings of beads and sequins or a star shape will all look exquisite!

The Luckiest Fairy

It's one very lucky fairy's birthday today, and she has received a special invitation from the King and Queen of Fairyland to attend a banquet at the palace tonight! Can you work out who she is by following the clues? When you think you know, write her name at the bottom.

This fairy loves blustery days!

She likes to wear her auburn hair loose.

This fairy is wearing a pendant around her neck!

She prefers shoes to boots.

This fairy always wears sunny yellow.

The birthday fairy is...
Abigail

Special Spells

The naughty goblins are spying on Goldie and Ruby as they practise their spells in the skies above Fairyland! Colour this picture in using your favourite pens or pencils.

If I could be a fairy for a day, I would turn...

into a...

I promise to turn them back to normal again afterwards!

Magical Animals and their Fairies!

Seven Magical Animals were captured by Jack Frost, but managed to escape and hide in the human world. It was up to Rachel and Kirsty to reunite them. Their stories are filled with excitement, and here's a good place to find out a bit about each one!

Ashley the Dragon Fairy

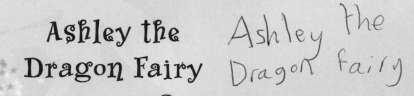

Each Magical Animal Fairy looks after a special power. Ashley's dragon, Sizzle, is responsible for the power of our imagination.

Erin the Firebird Fairy

Erin the Firebird Fairy is looking after a very special animal, a firebird called Giggles! She helps make everybody laugh.

Lara the Black Cat Fairy

Here is Lara, the Black Cat Fairy. She is holding her special Magical Animal, a little cat called Lucky, who is responsible for spreading good luck.

rihanna
the sea horse
fairy

Rihanna the Seahorse Fairy

This beautiful fairy is called Rihanna, and she is the Seahorse Fairy. Her special Magical Animal is a tiny seahorse called Bubbles. He helps people to enjoy wonderful friendships.

Sophia the Snow
swan fairy

Sophia the Snow Swan Fairy

Don't you love Sophia the Snow Swan Fairy's gorgeous dress? Her special creature is a swan named Belle. Belle helps to spread compassion, or kindness.

caitlin the ice
Bear fairy

Caitlin the Ice Bear Fairy

Brrr! It's chilly in this Rainbow Magic fairy's world. Caitlin is the Ice Bear Fairy, and her Magical Animal is a little furry bear called Crystal. She has the special power to spread courage. It's easy to feel brave around Crystal!

leona the
unicorn
fairy

Leona the Unicorn Fairy

Leona's Magical Animal looks like a tiny horse. Twisty is a unicorn with special healing powers to spread around Fairyland and the human world.

Petal Puzzle

How well do you know the Petal Fairies? Test your knowledge by answering the questions and filling in the puzzle below.

ACROSS

4 Jack Frost steals a magic _____ from each of the fairies.

6 Does Charlotte the Sunflower Fairy wear trousers or a dress?

7 Name of the Daisy Fairy

DOWN

1 The name of the Poppy Fairy

2 The name of the Walker family's pet dog

3 Where does Jack Frost want to grow flowers?

4 The colour of Ella the Rose Fairy's dress

5 The surname of Rachel Walker's best friend

Pink Petals!

Ella the Rose Fairy was giggling while you were doing the crossword puzzle opposite. She knew all the answers! Here's a picture of her for you to colour in lots of shades of pink.

Fairy Ring Pairs

This is a good game to play with a friend, although you can play alone too, if you'd rather! It's all about matching fairies as fast as you can. If you have a stop watch, or a watch with a second hand, it might be useful.

How to play

- First of all, each player should choose which row of fairies they would like to find.

- Now place the book in front of you both, and start to search for the matching fairies below as quickly as you can. But the game's not over then!

- Now you've got to find the four hiding goblins, and Jack Frost!

- The winner is the player who finds all her fairies and the goblins and Jack Frost the fastest!

- Shout "I'm the fastest in Fairyland" when you've found everyone!

You can play again by swapping rows, or turn the book upside down to make it harder!

Row A

Row B

Fairyland Treasure Hunt

The King and Queen of Fairyland have set you and your friends a challenge. The items on this list can be found in most gardens or parks. Whoever can find the most things is the winner! Tick the box beside each one when you've collected it.

Message from Queen Titania:

Make sure you ask an adult to go with you and your friends.

1 feather, for tickling goblins.

3 pebbles to paint and give
as gifts to your fairy hosts.

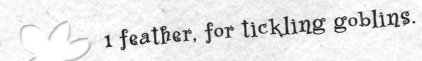

6 blades of green grass,
to tie up parcels.

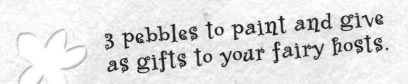

1 pink flower, as a gift for
Queen Titania (always ask a
grown-up before picking any
flowers!).

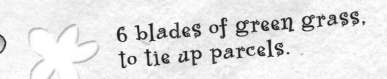

1 acorn or nutshell to fill with
petals or other special things.

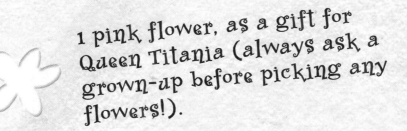

PS: If you ever receive an invitation to Fairyland, make sure you
take all these things with you – they're sure to be useful!

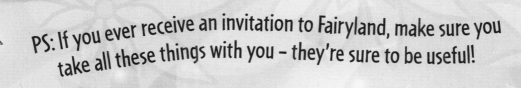

August Birthday Girls

School's out and it's the holidays – sun-soaked August, we love you!

1st-12th
Sky the Blue Fairy

Whether holidaying with best friends or staying closer to home, you're always jolly and bright. There'll be all kinds of smiley surprises in the year ahead!

13th-22nd
Kylie the Carnival Fairy

My birthday girls love dressing in dazzling costumes and soaking up the limelight. This year try helping out backstage too. You might just discover some impressive hidden talents!

23rd-31st
Summer the Holiday Fairy

When you're around, it feels like the sun is shining, even when the weather outside is dreary! August birthday girls enjoy starting new collections, so what about badges or seashells?

Birthstone

The peridot is the birthstone for August. A stunning green colour, it is often used in pretty jewellery.

Goldie's Summer Refresher!

On a hot sunny day there is nothing more refreshing than a glass of lemonade. It's easy to make it yourself – Goldie always has a cool glass to offer her friends. Even Jack Frost likes it, as long as there are lots of ice cubes!

What you'll need:

3 large lemons
150g granulated sugar
1.4 litres of water

This will make around 1.7 litres of lemonade. Enough for a lot of thirsty fairy friends!

The zest of the lemon contains most of the flavour!

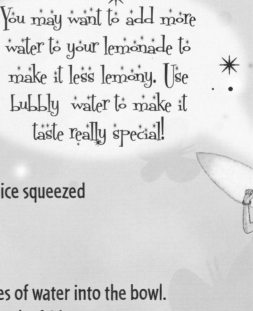

You may want to add more water to your lemonade to make it less lemony. Use bubbly water to make it taste really special!

1. Before you start, make sure you ask an adult to help you.

2. Wash the lemons in warm water, and then, using a zester or potato peeler, remove just the coloured part of the skin: the zest.

3. Put the zest into a large bowl and add the juice squeezed from all the lemons.

4. Add the sugar to the zest and juice.

5. Ask an adult to boil a kettle and pour 1.4 litres of water into the bowl. Stir well, cover, and leave overnight to cool in the fridge.

6. When your lemonade is cold, sieve it to remove any pips and pour into bottles!

Race from the Rain!

It's the Fairyland Race today, and everyone wants to finish before Hayley the Rain Fairy arrives! Find a friend to play with, and get started. You'll need a coin each and a dice. Whoever throws the highest number on the first throw starts. You can play as many times as you like, use the scorecards to record who wins!

Abigail the Breeze Fairy is helping you to fly along! Whizz on five spaces.

You forgot to curtsey to Queen Titania before you set off! Go back to the start.

START

A pesky goblin has turned the signpost round. Go back three spaces.

Scorecard 1

You're feeling very hungry. Stop for a snack and miss a turn.

Melodie's Musical Maze

Poor Melodie has become lost in the maze at the Fairyland Gardens! With your finger, trace a route that leads Melodie out of the maze.

Dress Design

This fairy needs an amazing outfit to wear to the king and queen's party. Can you design and draw something gorgeous? Don't forget the accessories!

September Birthday Girls

September's the month to play with school friends in the hazy autumn sunshine!

1st-12th
Saffron the Yellow Fairy

September girls are top team players! If you're not a sporting star yet, maybe you haven't found the right game for you. Why not try having fun on a netball court or taking on a table tennis match?

13th-22nd
Katie the Kitten Fairy

A purr-fect afternoon for you is to snuggle on a cosy sofa with a bar of chocolate and a girlie DVD. Why not invite a friend next time? Chilling on your own is fun, but friend-time is twice as nice!

23rd-30th
Sophie the Sapphire Fairy

When your friends fall out, they turn to you. You're a calm, lovable peacemaker with a special knack for turning frowns upside down! Keep up the good work and you'll soon be the most popular girl in town!

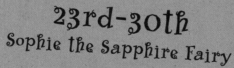

Birthstone

A fountain of blue sparkles flash around Sophie's stunning sapphire. This birthstone is a gorgeous glittery gem.

Almost Bedtime!

Meet Willow the Wednesday Fairy! She has had a very busy day and is looking forward to going to bed. But the goblins have been casting pesky spells! Look very carefully and try to find five things that you don't normally spot in a bedroom! Circle each one as you find it.

Magical Ribbon Rescue

Kirsty Tate and her friend Rachel Walker were on their way to the fiesta that was being held at the village hall. They couldn't wait to see all the costumes and dancing! They were also hoping for an adventure. Rachel was staying with Kirsty's family for half-term and they were helping the Dance Fairies find their missing magical ribbons. The Dance Ribbons helped dancers perform their best throughout Fairyland as well as all around the human world, but Jack Frost had stolen the ribbons in order to make sure his goblin servants would dance well at his parties.

The fairy king and queen had heard about the stolen ribbons, and they'd been to Jack Frost's castle to get them back. Unfortunately, he'd seen them coming and had cast a spell to hurl all the ribbons into the human world, with a goblin to guard each one.

The problem with the ribbons being missing was that dancing was going wrong in Fairyland, and all over the world! Luckily, Kirsty and Rachel had helped the fairies find the Ballet, Disco, Rock 'n' Roll, Tap Dance and Jazz Ribbons.

"The Salsa Ribbon is still lost," Kirsty said, as they walked to the hall where the fiesta was taking place. She glanced around. "I hope the goblin with the Salsa Ribbon turns up," she said quietly. "That way we might be able to get the ribbon away from him and safely back to Saskia the Salsa Fairy," she added. "If we don't, the salsa dancing is going to be ruined today!"

As Rachel and Kirsty walked along, they came across a group of their friends gathered around a papier-mâché piñata dangling from a tree branch. Everyone was taking it in turns to hit it, hoping to release the goodies inside. Kirsty saw Lucy, one of her school friends.

"Do you want to have a go?" Lucy asked.

"Ooh, yes, please," Kirsty said at once.

Rachel helped tie a blindfold around her eyes and handed her the stick. Kirsty bashed the piñata as hard as she could. *Crack!* It  split open and sweets, small toys and glitter tumbled onto the ground. Rachel noticed a tiny spark of light shoot out of the piñata and up into the air.

"That's strange!" Rachel said to herself, and then an exciting thought struck her – could it be a fairy?

Rachel watched closely as the sparkle zipped around. Not wanting to lose sight of the glowing light, she raced after it, heart thumping. Then she smiled. It was Saskia the Salsa Fairy! She was perched on the edge of a roof, waving at her. Rachel waved back with a grin, just as Kirsty came around the corner with a handful of sweets.

"Look, Kirsty," she whispered, pointing up at Saskia.

Saskia fluttered down, and Kirsty saw that she had long black hair, pinned back with a beautiful red rose, and she was wearing a red top and a red skirt with gorgeous orange ruffles.

"Hello!" the fairy said, smiling. "I'm here to find my ribbon. I have to get it back so that all the dancing in the fiesta goes well today!"

You can read more about this adventure in **Saskia the Salsa Fairy**

Animal Search

Can you find the name of the Pet Keeper Fairies and their animals hidden somewhere in this jumble of letters? The words could be hidden up, down, forwards, backwards or even diagonally, so look carefully!

```
H A E N P N E R U A L
P I I E P L G H E T A
T A N E R E A E S C F
S N U G O R M I S T Y
Y G G R R E M M I H S
K L G I N C K E N L A
R I E L K N I W T B H
A T K I R U L T E R S
P T L K M O L L Y I A
S E T L Y B L I E T L
N R I N K A T I E R F
```

Bella   Penny   Katie
Misty   Glitter   Shimmer   Lauren
                                       Bouncer

Harriet   Georgia   Molly
Twinkle   Sparky   Flash

Lemon Scented Secrets

When fairies want to write secret messages to each other without the goblins being able to read them, they use invisible ink. Try it yourself, but first ask an adult to help because you need to use the oven.

You will need:

1 lemon
Saucer
Paintbrush
Sheet of white paper

1. Ask an adult to turn the oven on to 120°C or gas mark 2.

2. Squeeze the lemon juice onto your saucer.

3. Dip a paint brush into the lemon juice and write your message on the paper.

4. When you (or a friend) want to read the message, ask an adult to place it on the top shelf of the oven and then remove after 5 minutes. Now you can read your magical message!

A Shivery Scene

This is a picture of Jack Frost's Ice Castle. Brave fairies sometimes venture up the icy path to invite Jack Frost to parties, but they don't stay long as it's so cold. Brrr! Have a good look at this chilly scene, then turn over the page and answer as many of the questions as you can without peeping!

How much do you remember?

1. How many geese did you count?
2. What is the goblin doing?
3. What colour is the goblin's hat?
4. How many brave fairies are in the picture?
5. What is the goblin sitting on?
6. How many windows did you count in the Ice Castle?

A Freezing Flag

While we are still shivering away near Jack Frost's Ice Castle, there is one more thing that needs to be done. Can you help to design a flag that he can fly from the top? There are some ideas below.

Beautiful Bridesmaid

Doesn't Mia the Bridesmaid Fairy look pretty? If you study these four pictures very carefully you'll see that one of them is slightly different from the others. Can you work out which is the odd one out?

A.

B.

C.

D.

Summer Memories

Are you having a good summer? It's always nice to keep a diary, or record fun things that happen. There's a special place for you to do that here. In a year's time, it might be nice to look back and remember what a great time you had!

Today's date: ~~Saturday~~ 1-6-2013

My name is: Sophie

My best friend is called: Lottie

My favourite day of the summer so far: 28-6-2013

Why it was so special: I went to Butlins

What I am looking forward to most: going to camp

My favourite outfit for summer:

My favourite summertime treat:

Magical Masks

If you're having a birthday party this month, why not ask your guests to create and wear their own magical masks? Or you could make these together at the party!

1. On a piece of card, draw a face outline that is slightly bigger than your own.

2. Cut the shape out and hold it up to your face, then mark where the eyes should go. Ask a grown-up to carefully snip out almond-shaped peep holes.

3. Hold the mask back up to your face, then sketch where the nose sits. Now carefully cut off the bottom half of the mask so that your mouth becomes visible.

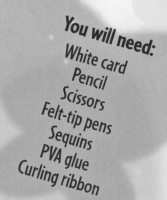

4. Use your brightest felt-tip pens to decorate the mask with hearts, butterflies and stars.

5. Stick sequins onto your mask, creating pretty patterns around the eyes.

6. Now make a small hole on either side of the fairy mask.

7. Thread a long piece of curling ribbon through one of the holes and tie it in a knot at the back of the mask. Repeat on the other side, then tie the ends together behind your head.

8. Take the mask off, then ask a grown-up to curl the ribbon ends with the scissors.

You will need:
White card
Pencil
Scissors
Felt-tip pens
Sequins
PVA glue
Curling ribbon

More Fairy Magic!

Fiona the Flute Fairy has made a special wish, and is flying to deliver it to Chrissie the Wish Fairy. She has written it in special fairy code, because there are goblins about and she wants her wish to be secret!
Can you read her wish by using the special code below?

A ♥
B ✿
C 🐝
D ◈
E ⭐
F 🍄
G 🏰

H ❋
I ◈
J 💧
K 🧁
L 🐸
M 🌙
N 🎈

O 🌸
P ⚡
Q 💎
R 🍒
S 🦋
T ☁️
U 🎵

V 🪄
W 🍃
X ⭕
Y 🦋
Z 🎀

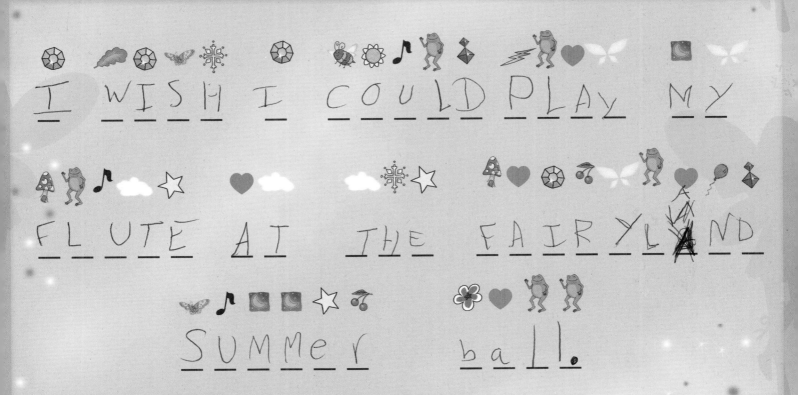

I WISH I COULD PLAY MY

FLUTE AT THE FAIRYLAND

SUMMER ball.

Garden Fun

Charlotte the Sunflower Fairy would like to show you how to have lots of fun with flowers and plants. Here's how to grow your own sunflowers! Plant seeds in little pots on your windowsill, then give them to your friends!

First collect...

Empty yoghurt pots   Compost
Poster paint   Sunflower seeds
Paintbrush   Plastic food bags
Stickers or ribbon   Lolly sticks
Felt-tip pens

1   Cover the yoghurt pots with brightly coloured poster paint. Stand the pots upside down to dry.

2   Decorate the pots with cute stickers, or tie a ribbon round them in a bow.

3   Fill each pot with compost and make a hole with your thumb about 2cm deep.

4   Pop one seed into the hole and cover it with compost. Sprinkle a little water on the top.

5   Carefully put the pots into clear plastic food bags and seal them up. This will help the seeds stay warm. Store your pots in a dry, dark place.

6   When the first leaves begin to bud, remove the bags and put the pots on a sunny windowsill. Don't forget to give them a little water every day.

7   Write each of your guests' names on a wooden lolly stick and push them into the pots. Your gifts are ready to be handed out!

Don't forget to tell your friends to look after their seedlings! When the plants reach 10cm tall they can be planted out in the garden. Which one of you can grow the tallest flower?

Did You Know...

There are so many creatures in Fairyland that we have here in the human world too, and the fairies know some amazing things about all of them...

A bee's wings beat an amazing 11,400 times a minute!

Don't worry if you have an untamed garden with lots of wild flowers and grasses – butterflies will love it!

You might not like nettles much because they sting, but they make a royal banquet for caterpillars, which will then turn into beautiful butterflies!

It takes 12 weeks for frogspawn to turn into froglets (baby frogs). Look! It's me when I was a baby!

There are around 25,000 different species of bee in the human world!

My roses produce flowers every year, but did you know that there's a plant in the human world called Puya raimondii that only produces flowers every 150 years, and then it dies! Sounds like Jack Frost might have cast a spell on it!

Rainbow Magic!

It's the end of another fabulous day in Fairyland, and the king and queen have come to say goodbye, and thank you for visiting. Colour in this amazing scene!

How to be a Good Fairy

Grace the Glitter Fairy has waved her sparkly wand over this page to present you with these ten Rainbow Magic promises. Are you ready to whisper these wise fairy words?

Be kind to everyone

Even frosty folk can melt when they're greeted with a friendly face and a smile.

Spread the magic

Write spells, sing songs and make wands to wave. Fairies love tiaras, wings and anything sparkly!

Put friends first

Always be there for any friend who needs you, and they'll be there for you.

Look after animals

Animals can see fairies too! Be kind to pets and respect animals of all shapes and sizes.

Little things mean a lot

A home-made birthday gift, a tiny note or a thoughtful phone call can show just how much you care.

Everyone's invited!

Rainbow Fairies always play and work as a team. It's surprising what you can do if you stick together!

Be happy to help

Always volunteer before you are asked and your acts of friendship will never be forgotten.

Laugh, play and celebrate

Never let a birthday or special occasion pass you by!

See the beauty in nature

Look closely and you'll discover that the sparkling dew on the morning grass is actually thousands of tiny diamonds scattered by a Jewel Fairy.

Rainbow Magic is all around!

Never forget that Rainbow Magic is the magic shimmering inside you. Believe in yourself and no obstacle will ever be able to stand in your way.

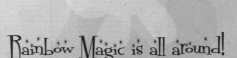

Answers

Page 18
Spot the Difference

Page 19
Goblin Tangle
There are 15 goblins in the tangle.

Pages 20-21
Eye Spy

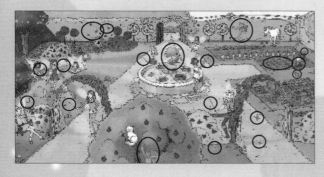

Page 22
Spot the Fairies!
The four fairies appear in Row C.

Page 24
The birthday fairy is
Abigail the Breeze fairy!

Page 28
Petal Puzzle

Page 38
Melodie's Musical Maze

Page 41
Almost Bedtime!

Page 46
Magical Animal Search

H	A	E	N	P	N	E	R	U	A	L		
P	I	I	E	P	L	G	H	E	T	A		
T	A	N	E	R	E	A	E	S	C	F		
S	N	U	G	O	R	M	I	S	T	Y		
Y	G	G	R	E	M	M	I	H	S			
K	L	G	I	N	C	K	E	N	L	A		
R	I	E	L	K	N	I	W	T	B	H		
A	T	K	I	R	U	L	T	E	R	S		
P	S	T	L	K	M	O	L	L	Y	I	A	
S	N	E	T	L	Y	B	L	I	E	T	L	
N	R	I	N	K	A	T	I	E	R	F		

Pages 48-49
A Shivery Scene
1. Three
2. Fishing
3. Yellow and red stripes
4. One
5. A tree stump
6. One

Page 52
Beautiful Bridesmaid
The odd one out is C. The charms are
missing from Mia's bracelet.

Page 55
More Fairy Magic!
Wish says: I wish I could play my
flute at the Fairyland Summer Ball.

Meet all the Rainbow Magic fairies in these exciting storybooks!

The Rainbow Fairies

Ruby the Red Fairy - 978-1-84362-0167
Amber the Orange Fairy - 978-1-84362-0174
Saffron the Yellow Fairy - 978-1-84362-0181
Fern the Green Fairy - 978-1-84362-0198
Sky the Blue Fairy - 978-1-84362-0204
Izzy the Indigo Fairy - 978-1-84362-0211
Heather the Violet Fairy - 978-1-84362-0228

The Weather Fairies

Crystal the Snow Fairy - 978-1-84362-633-6
Abigail the Breeze Fairy - 978-1-84362-634-3
Pearl the Cloud Fairy - 978-1-84362-635-0
Goldie the Sunshine Fairy - 978-1-84362-641-1
Evie the Mist Fairy - 978-1-84362-636-7
Storm the Lightning Fairy - 978-1-84362-637-4
Hayley the Rain Fairy - 978-1-84362-638-1

The Party Fairies

Cherry the Cake Fairy - 978-1-84362-818-7
Melodie the Music Fairy - 978-1-84362-819-4
Grace the Glitter Fairy - 978-1-84362-820-0
Honey the Sweet Fairy - 978-1-84362-821-7
Polly the Party Fun Fairy - 978-184362-822-4
Phoebe the Fashion Fairy - 978-184362-823-1
Jasmine the Present Fairy - 978-1-84362-824-8

The Jewel Fairies

India the Moonstone Fairy - 978-1-84362-958-0
Scarlett the Garnet Fairy - 978-1-84362-954-2
Emily the Emerald Fairy - 978-1-84362-955-9
Chloe the Topaz Fairy - 978-1-84362-956-6
Amy the Amethyst Fairy - 978-1-84362-957-3
Sophie the Sapphire Fairy - 978-184362-953-5
Lucy the Diamond Fairy - 978-1-84362-959-7

The Pet Keeper Fairies

Katie the Kitten Fairy - 978-1-84616-166-7
Bella the Bunny Fairy - 978-1-84616-170-4
Georgia the Guinea Pig Fairy - 978-1-84616-168-1
Lauren the Puppy Fairy - 978-1-84616-169-8
Harriet the Hamster Fairy - 978-1-84616-167-4
Molly the Goldfish Fairy - 978-1-84616-172-8
Penny the Pony Fairy - 978-1-84616-171-1

The Fun Day Fairies

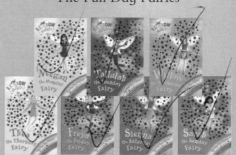

Megan the Monday Fairy - 978-1-84616-188-9
Tallulah the Tuesday Fairy - 978-1-84616-189-6
Willow the Wednesday Fairy - 978-1-84616-190-2
Thea the Thursday Fairy - 978-1-84616-191-9
Freya the Friday Fairy - 978-1-84616-192-6
Sienna the Saturday Fairy - 978-1-84616-193-3
Sarah the Sunday Fairy - 978-1-84616-194-0

The Petal Fairies

Tia the Tulip Fairy - 978-1-84616-457-6
Pippa the Poppy Fairy - 978-1-84616-458-3
Louise the Lily Fairy - 978-1-84616-459-0
Charlotte the Sunflower Fairy - 978-184616-460-6
Danielle the Daisy Fairy - 978-1-84616-462-0
Olivia the Orchid Fairy - 978-1-84616-461-3
Ella the Rose Fairy - 978-1-84616-464-4

The Dance Fairies

Bethany the Ballet Fairy- 978-1-84616-490-3
Jade the Disco Fairy - 978-1-84616-491-0
Rebecca the Rock 'N' Roll Fairy -978-1-84616-492-7
Tasha the Tap Dance Fairy - 978-1-84616-493-4
Jessica the Jazz Fairy - 978-1-84616-495-8
Saskia the Salsa Fairy - 978-1-84616-496-5
Imogen the Ice Dance Fairy - 978-1-84616-497-2

The Sporty Fairies

Helena the Horseriding Fairy - 978-1-84616-888-8
Francesca the Football Fairy - 978-1-84616-889-5
Zoe the Skating Fairy - 978-1-84616-890-1
Naomi the Netball Fairy - 978-1-84616-891-8
Samantha the Swimming Fairy - 978-184616-892-5
Alice the Tennis Fairy - 978-184616-893-2
Gemma the Gymnastics Fairy - 978-184616-894-9

The Music Fairies

Poppy the Piano Fairy – 978-140830-033-6
Ellie the Guitar Fairy – 978-140830-030-5
Fiona the Flute Fairy – 978-140830-029-9
Danni the Drum Fairy – 978-140830-028-2
Maya the Harp Fairy – 978-1-40830-031-2
Victoria the Violin Fairy – 978-1-40830-027-5
Sadie the Saxophone Fairy – 978-1-40830-032-9

The Magical Animal Fairies

Ashley the Dragon Fairy – 978-1-40830-349-8
Lara the Black Cat Fairy – 978-1-40830-350-4
Erin the Firebird Fairy – 978-1-40830-351-1
Rihanna the Seahorse Fairy – 978-1-40830-352-8
Sophia the Snow Swan Fairy – 978-140830-353-5
Leona the Unicorn Fairy – 978-1-40830-354-2
Caitlin the Ice Bear Fairy – 978-1-40830-355-9

The Green Fairies

Nicole the Beach Fairy – 978-1-40830-474-7
Isabella the Air Fairy – 978-1-40830-475-4
Edie the Garden Fairy – 978-1-40830-476-1
Coral the Reef Fairy – 978-1-40830-477-8
Lily the Rainforest Fairy – 978-1-40830-478-5
Milly the River Fairy – 978-1-40830-480-8
Carrie the Snow Cap Fairy – 978-1-40830-479-2

The Ocean Fairies

Ally the Dolphin Fairy – 978-1-40830-815-8
Amelie the Seal Fairy – 978-1-40830-816-5
Pia the Penguin Fairy – 978-1-40830-817-2
Stephanie the Starfish Fairy – 978-1-40830-819-6
Tess the Sea Turtle Fairy – 978-1-40830-818-9
Whitney the Whale Fairy – 978-1-40830-820-2
Courtney the Clownfish Fairy – 978-1-40830-821-9

The Specials

Holly the Christmas Fairy – 978-1-84362-661-9
Summer the Holiday Fairy – 978-184362-960-3
Stella the Star Fairy – 978-1-84616-919-9
Kylie the Carnival Fairy – 978-1-84616-175-9
Paige the Pantomine Fairy – 978-1-84616-209-1
Flora the Fancy Dress Fairy – 978-1-84616-505-4
Chrissie the Wish Fairy – 978-1-84616-506-1
Shannon the Ocean Fairy – 978-1-40830-025-1
Gabriella the Snow Kingdom Fairy – 978-1-40830-034-3
Mia the Bridesmaid Fairy – 978-1-40830-348-1
Destiny the Pop Star Fairy – 978-1-40830-473-0
Juliet the Valentine Fairy – 978-1-40831-135-6
Belle the Birthday Fairy – 978-1-40830-810-3

Choose your own Magic titles

Ruby the Red Fairy – 978-1-40830-789-2
Katie and the Missing Kitten – 978-1-40830-812-7

All priced at £3.99. The Specials are priced at £5.99.
Rainbow Magic books are available from all good bookshops,
or can be ordered direct from the publisher: Orchard Books,
PO BOX 29, Douglas IM99 1BQ.
Credit card orders please telephone 01624 836000
or fax 01624 837033 or visit our website: www.orchardbooks.co.uk
or e-mail: bookshop@enterprise.net for details.

To order please quote title, author and ISBN and your full name
and address. Cheques and postal orders should be made payable
to 'Bookpost plc.'
Postage and packing is FREE within the UK
(overseas customers should add £2.00 per book).
Prices and availability are subject to change.